susannah

a musical drama in two acts, ten scenes

libretto and music by
carlisle floyd

vocal score by the composer

winner of the New York Music Critics' Award for the *Best Opera in 1956*

boosey and hawkes

The composer wishes to acknowledge gratefully the invaluable contribution of Phyllis Curtin, both for her unfailing belief in the opera and for her laudable creation of the title role.

fourth edition
corrected and revised 1997

1967 edition of vocal score edited by
Ross Reimueller

cover design by Evon Streetman

cast

SUSANNAH POLK	*Soprano*
SAM POLK, her brother	*Tenor*
OLIN BLITCH, an evangelist	*Bass-baritone*
LITTLE BAT McLEAN	*Tenor*
ELDER McLEAN	*Baritone*
ELDER GLEATON	*Tenor*
ELDER HAYES	*Tenor*
ELDER OTT	*Baritone*
MRS. McLEAN	*Mezzo-soprano*
MRS. GLEATON	*Soprano*
MRS. HAYES	*Soprano*
MRS. OTT	*Contralto*
PEOPLE OF NEW HOPE VALLEY	*Singers & Dancers*

setting

NEW HOPE VALLEY, TENNESSEE

time

THE RECENT PAST

The story of "Susannah"

The musical drama has as its basis the Apocryphal book of the same name, with the locale transferred to a Tennessee mountain valley in the recent past, a credible setting for the primitive religion with which it deals. The story tells of the Elders' discovery of Susannah bathing in the creek which is sought as a baptismal font. The Elders, because of lust and the guilt accompanying this emotion, brand Susannah as evil and "of the devil," and set forth to announce their discovery to the valley's people and to the visiting evangelist, Olin Blitch. Rumor, elaboration, and lies quickly supplant fact, and Susannah is soon an outcast. At a revival meeting Susannah is called upon publicly by Blitch to confess and repent, and when she refuses she is pursued to her home by Blitch, who is still convinced of her guilt and reputation for lechery. He fails to force a confession and Susannah, exhausted and broken, succumbs to his advances and is seduced by him. Blitch, thus discovering her innocence, becomes a man bereft of his spiritual support and terrified by his image of a vengeful God. He summons the Elders and their wives to the church and, with Susannah present, attempts to convince them of her true story without implicating himself. Remaining implacable and unbelieving, they leave, and Blitch, pitiable and anguished, throws himself upon Susannah's mercy, which is denied. Susannah's brother, Sam, pries the story of Blitch's misdemeanor from her. Enraged, he leaves the house, shoots and kills Blitch at the creek where he is baptizing. The people of the valley come after Susannah, menacing and warning her to leave the valley. Susannah greets them unflinchingly with wild and derisive laughter, and when they advance she disperses them with the threat of a gun. Little Bat, weak and malevolent son of Elder McLean who earlier implicated Susannah by confessing falsely that he had been intimate with her, enters fearfully observing the scene and is cajoled by Susannah into embracing her. As he puts his arms around her, she slaps him viciously, thus severing forever her last tie with her community and her world. She is left an inexorably lonely and embittered woman.

WORLD PREMIERE
FLORIDA STATE UNIVERSITY
TALLAHASSEE, FLORIDA
FEBRUARY 24, 1955

NEW YORK PREMIERE
NEW YORK CITY OPERA
NEW YORK CITY
SEPTEMBER 27, 1956

Phyllis Curtin	SUSANNAH POLK	*Phyllis Curtin*
Walter James	SAM POLK	*Jon Crain*
Mack Harrell	OLIN BLITCH	*Norman Treigle*
Eb Thomas	LITTLE BAT McLEAN	*Eb Thomas*
Harrison Fisher	ELDER McLEAN	*Arthur Newman*
Kenneth Nelson	ELDER GLEATON	*Gregory Millar*
Dayton Smith	ELDER HAYES	*John Druary*
Lee Liming	ELDER OTT	*Joshua Hecht*
Martha Kay Willis	MRS. McLEAN	*Irene Kramarich*
Catherine Murphy	MRS. GLEATON	*Sara Fleming*
Joan Nichy	MRS. HAYES	*Olivia Bonelli*
Bette Jo Armstrong	MRS. OTT	*Mignon Dunn*
Karl Kuersteiner	CONDUCTOR	*Erich Leinsdorf*
Lynn Orr	STAGE DIRECTOR	*Leo Kerz*
Franklin Adams	DESIGNER	*Leo Kerz*

instrumentation

2 FLUTES *(2nd doubling Piccolo)*
2 OBOES *(2nd doubling English Horn)*
2 CLARINETS *(2nd doubling Bass Clarinet)*
2 BASSOONS *(2nd doubling Contra Bassoon)*

4 HORNS
2 TRUMPETS
3 TROMBONES
1 TUBA

TIMPANI
SNARE DRUM
CYMBALS
GONG
XYLOPHONE

CELESTE
HARP

STRINGS

Performance materials are available from the Boosey & Hawkes Rental Library. Application for license to perform should be made to Boosey & Hawkes.

A reduced orchestration is available on rental.

duration

105 MINUTES, IN TWO ACTS.

TO MY MOTHER AND FATHER

SUSANNAH
ACT ONE

OPENING MUSIC

TEXT AND MUSIC
By
CARLISLE FLOYD

B Largamente ma l'istesso tempo (♩ =104)

Scene One

Scene: New Hope Valley in the mountains of Tennessee. It is a Monday night in mid-July, and a square dance is in progress in the yard of New Hope Church. A fiddler and caller are in the background, and downstage are the participants in the dance, the people of the community as on-lookers, the Elders and their wives. At the curtain's rise, the dance is underway. Susannah, a young girl of uncommon beauty, is conspicuous in the group by virtue of a brightly-colored dress and the gravitation of men to her square. Her face is flushed with high spirits and excitement, and she is unaware of the eyes upon her. It is early evening, and oil lanterns, hanging from trees, have been lit.

Allegro giocoso (♩=104))

PIANO

simile

quasi pizz.

MRS. GLEATON

Mrs. Gleaton

It's a

(To dancers, immediately assuming role of moral arbiter for the community)

11 **Meno mosso** (♩.=54)

sume your step-pin' un-der the eye of the Lord and let noth-in' pass bet-ween y', what y'

(The music and the dancing begin again. The Elders bring Blitch downstage to the wives, and there are pantomimed introductions and handshakings after which they all turn to watch the dancing. Susannah is once more the center of attention.)

12 **Allegro giocoso** (♩=104)

would-n't want Him to see, for the Lord se-eth all.

(After a moment in which he has watched Susannah intently)

McLEAN

McLean

BLITCH

Su -

Blitch

Who's the pret-ty one there in the mid-dle that's git-tin' all the boys?

marcato

quasi pizz.

san-nah Polk, who was raised by her broth-er what don't draw a sob - er breath. He's a

trif - lin' one, that Sam is. (Sam Polk, that's the name he was give.) He just hunts an' traps an' fish-es all day an' is

GLEATON
They're

al-lers drunk at night.

BLITCH
Let's pray for his soul an' his sis-ter's. I'll pray for 'em both to-night.

⑭ Tempo I

OTT

Ott

BLITCH *(After watching a while longer)*   They'd be pleased to have y', I'm sure.

Blitch

Think I'll join the young folks.   Ain't danced in quite   a spell.

(Blitch goes into the group and eventually makes his way to Susannah's square. The dancers in her square stop, stare, and Susannah's partner eagerly gives his place to Blitch. Susannah is shy, then as Blitch extends his hand, she smiles, and the square begins dancing again.)

Scene Two

Scene: Later the same evening. The scene is the front of the Polk farm house at stage left which possesses a rickety porch and steps. There are unpainted porchboxes of geraniums and petunias and tattered curtains in the windows. There are also an old rocker and a rusty plow point on the porch. The stage is dimly lit and quietness should pervade the scene.

(Susannah and Little Bat enter. Susannah is still radiant with excitement. Little Bat is a shifty-eyed youth, not too strong mentally. He possesses instead a litheness and feline quality of movement which, coupled with his eyes, gives him a constantly expectant and alert air. He looks about him furtively upon entering. It should be apparent from the beginning of the scene that he worships Susannah.)

B.H.BK.371

They both laugh, and then there is a pause while Susannah looks up into the night.

stepped on my feet so much o' the time, they're bound to turn black an' blue.

19 Adagio sostenuto (♩= 50)

Ain't it a pret-ty night!

The sky's so dark and vel-vet-like and it's all lit up with stars. It's like a

great big mir-ror re-flect-in' fire-flies o-ver a pond.

più mosso (♩= 60)

Look at all them stars, Lit-tle Bat. The long-er y' look the more y' see. The

sky seems so heav-y with stars that it might fall right down out of heav-en and cov-er us

all up in one big blank-et of vel-vet all stitched with dia-mon's.

20 a tempo (♩=♩) (♩=60)

Ain't it a pret-ty night. Just think, those stars can all peep down an'

see way be-yond where we can: They can see way be-yond them moun-tains to

Nash-ville and Ashe-ville an' Knox-ville. I wond-er what it's like out there, out there be-yond them mount-ains where the

below B. H. BK. 371

B. H. BK. 371

take time.

skys so heav-y with stars to-night that it could fall right down out of heav-en an' cov-er us

pp e rubato

colla voce

molto ritardando

up, and cov-er us up, in one big blank-et of vel-vet and dia-mon's.

ppp *pp* *dim.*

(Sam has come on unobserved during Susannah's aria. At the end of
it, he says in echo to announce himself, "Ain't it a pretty night!" At
the sound of his voice Susannah looks up, surprised, while Little Bat
leaps to his feet, ready for immediate departure. It should be immediately apparent that the bond between the brother and sister is
one of loyalty, warmth and tenderness. Sam, the uncomprehended
poet and recluse, is gentle by nature and tragically passive, until
the one thing of beauty left in his life is attacked. He has the same
dark good looks as his sister and is in his thirties.)

(To little Bat who is edging off-stage)

(23) **Moderato** (♩ = 76)

Sam! when did y' come? I'll see y' to-mor-row night at the pic-nic sup-per.

veloce

SAM

Ain't it a pret-ty night.

Moderato (♩ = 76)

sfz ⟩ p *p* *agitato* *tr* *tr*

B. H. BK. 371

the hands, dance around the yard together, laughing and shrieking happily as they do so. Then laughing and breathing heavily from their exertion, they stagger to the steps and sit down. Their breathing is easier, and there is silence while they look up at

Scene Three

Scene: A woods close to the Polk place. It is the following morning.
(As the curtain rises, Susannah's voice is heard off-stage, humming the "Jaybird" song. There is also the less pronounced sound of water rushing over rocks. After some time, the Elders appear. They walk hesitantly, peering about them, obviously in search of something.)

(*Repeat only if necessitated by the mise-en-scène.)

accelerando

molto cresc.

(The Elders continue their search until Hayes suddenly looking up, shouts, "There it—!" His voice breaks off abruptly, and the other Elders look up and follow the direction of his raised arm. They all stand rooted in their tracks for some time, expressions of shock on

(29) Allegro largamente (♩ = 104)

HAYES

There it is!

veloce

their faces being gradually supplanted by those of lust. Eventually McLean shatters the moment when he realizes what he is feeling and doing, and draws himself up indignantly. At the sound of his voice, the other Elders, horrified and deeply disturbed, too, at what they have felt, quickly adopt his outraged tone and stance. They continue to look, however.)

sempre ff

(30) Andante con moto (♩ = 96)

HAYES

A - bath-in' in a pub-lic place!

McLEAN

It's an out-rage! It's a blas-phe-mous out-rage!

(30) Andante con moto (♩ = 96)

slowly, casting furtive glances in the direction of the pond. They chant as they leave the stage, their voices gradually receding into the distance until they are gone. When the stage is silent, we hear again the unsuspecting Susannah singing merrily to herself.)

Scene Four

Scene: The time is the same evening: the scene the same as in Scene I. Now, however, there is a long crude table upstage laden with food.
(Several women are at the table languidly keeping the flies away with fans made of paper-streamers tacked to broomhandles. There are people in knots of twos and threes pantomiming intense gossiping at the curtain's rise. The Elders' wives are once more downstage right, the Elders standing at stage left. There is a frail attempt at conviviality on the part of the young people who are oppressed by the hushed and foreboding atmosphere of the church ground.)

stringendo -

(The scene shifts to the Elders while the wives continue to pantomime their talking. Several men from the crowd have gathered around them.)

Hayes: same as what we said. She's got-ta make a pub-lic con-fes-sion or out o' the church she goes.

Ott: An' out-n the val-ley, too, may-be. She's a schem-in' one, she is. Young men ain't safe with her a-round. She's an in-stru-ment of the dev-il.

Gleaton: The preach-er's at Broth-er McLean's house now a-pray-in' that her soul might be saved, that she'll turn a-side from her e-vil ways an' be washed in the cleans-in' stream.

McLean: She's a

(During McLean's lines, Susannah comes in quietly upstage carrying a covered dish. She is unobserved at first, and then as she starts downstage, the conversation dies out as the various groups become aware of her presence.)

(By this time, Susannah has come downstage abreast of the Elders' wives, nodding "good evening" on her way. The people have returned her greetings in some cases with fear and distrust and in others with lofty disdain. Susannah's expression has changed from one of easy cordiality to alert questioning. Superficially, however, she remains warm and friendly.)

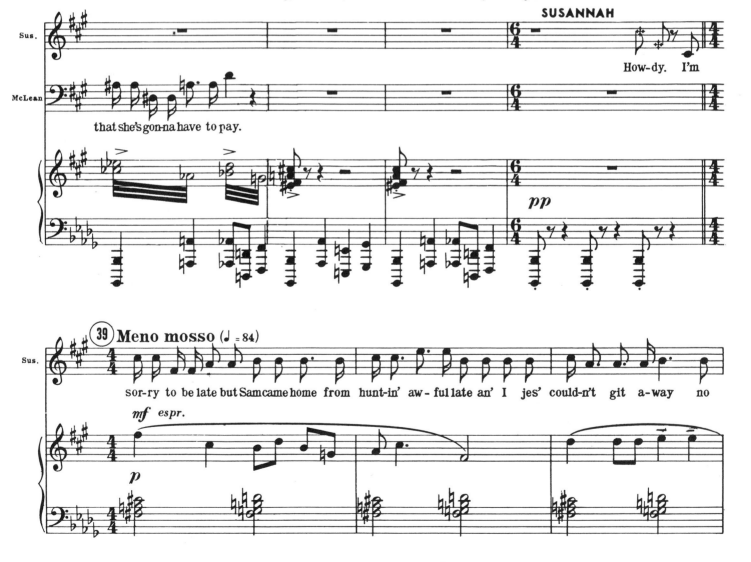

(The women nod stiffly without looking up There is total silence on the stage with all eyes on Susannah Susannah, embarrassed, attempts more conversation, constantly growing more uneasy under the steady scrutiny of the circle of eyes.)

soon-er.　　　　　　　　　　I brought a dish o' field peas.　I

(Still no response. She smiles only with her mouth now, faint flickers of smiles that hardly move her lips. Her eyes show only bewilderment and intense discomfort.)

picked an' shelled 'em this eve-nin' an' cooked 'em jest a bit a-go.　　　　　I'll jes'

(Nods to table)　　　　　　　　　　　　*(Crosses to table)*

sit 'em down o-ver here　if　that's all right.　　I　hope y' en-joy 'em.

(She sets the dish down on the table, and as she turns around she is caught in her motion by the stern voice of McLean.)

McLEAN

Su-san-nah,　　　you ain't wel-come here.

(*Susannah turns around slowly, looking hopefully from face to face, and in seeing no warmth in any of them, she brings her hand lightly up to her throat, and smiling weakly begins backing upstage. She says "excuse me" several times as she backs away, and then at the edge of the stage she clamps her fist over her mouth and runs. When she is gone, there is a long moment of strained silence, finally shattered by the clipped, strident voice of Mrs. McLean.*)

Scene Five

Scene: A half hour later.
(Susannah is seated on the front steps of the Polk house as in Scene Two, her face in her hands. After a moment, Little Bat stealthily creeps in from stage right, craning his neck to see if Susannah is alone. She becomes aware of him suddenly, and when she does, she leaps to her feet.)

SUSANNAH

Lit-tle Bat, what you do-in' here? He's in-side a-sleep

BAT

Is Sam here? I Tell me what? Tell me had to come tell y', Su-san-nah. I jes' had to come tell y'.

(He nods. She goes to him quickly and takes him by the shoulders.)

what? Oh, you was there to-night. What is it, Lit-tle Bat? What have I done?

My

made me say it, I swear they did, an' I was scairt, oh, Lord, I was scairt!

Git a-

way from here an' don' nev-er come back. Don't nev-er come back to this house! Git a-

(Little Bat runs off wailing and blubbering loudly. Susannah stands midstage with clenched

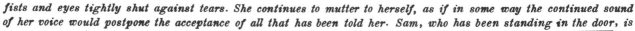

way, you ly-in' var-mint, an' don't y' nev-er come back! Git out!

fists and eyes tightly shut against tears. She continues to mutter to herself, as if in some way the continued sound of her voice would postpone the acceptance of all that has been told her. Sam, who has been standing in the door, is suddenly seen.)

Git out. Git out. Git out. Git out.

(Susannah continues to look deeply into Sam's eyes and gradually the realization comes to her that he has ceased

sempre accel.

talking and that there is nothing more he can say to mitigate her plight. She begins to cry, at first noiselessly, on-

ly her shoulders revealing her inner effort to control her tears. Eventually her face begins to break up, and finally throwing her arms around Sam's neck, sobbing, she cries with desperate intensity.)

51 Molto largamente (♩ = 76)

SUSANNAH

Sus. Sing me the "Jay-bird" song, ag-in.   Please sing me "Jay-bird", Sam.

A tempo, sempre cresc.

secco

Curtain

B. H. BK. 371

ACT TWO

Scene One

Scene: It is Friday morning.
(At the rise of the curtain, Sam is discovered leaning in the doorway of the Polk house with Susannah seated on the steps.
She is staring abstractedly as if she might have been in the same position for days. Sam watches her sadly while he smokes
his pipe. There is a long silence in which an atmosphere of static helplessness must be established.)

still don't feel no sin in me an' I cain't lie jes' fer them.

SAM *(Patiently)*
I know that, lit-tle rob - in. We

been through all that be-fore. The Lord, he knows what's in yer heart, so jes' don't fret no more.

㊾ **Allegro non troppo** (♩ = 84)

SUSANNAH
Meb-be I'm all they say I am. Meb-be the dev-il is in me. Meb-be he's hid-in' the sin I should feel. I

jes' don't know no more.

SAM *(Sharply)*
Shut up tal-kin' like that, Su-san-nah, an' don't y' think that way. That's

Scene Two

Scene: The same evening. The scene is the interior of New Hope church. There are rough-hewn benches and oil lamps suspended from the ceiling. There are also a crude pulpit which is slightly elevated, and an altar rail. There is a bench behind the pulpit which seats the choir. In the congregation are the Elders and their wives seated conspicuously, Little Bat with his parents. Also present are mothers, spraddle-legged, rocking babies on their knees, young children moving about, and generally an air of some confusion. In evidence everywhere are the paste-board fans, slowly in motion against the hot, still, July night air. Men are constantly removing bandannas and soggy handkerchiefs from hip-pockets to mop sweat from their faces. All this activity should be present, more or less, during the entire scene, increasing in speed and agitation as the scene builds into its climaxes.
(As the curtain rises, the action has already begun. The choir is singing lustily, and the preacher's voice is heard shouting over them. Two of the Elders are moving about the congregation with white, scarred dishpans, taking up the collection. Susannah, a small, huddled figure, sits alone on the last bench.
The scene in no way should be a parody but, instead, at all times should aim at projecting the tension, effrontery and, above all, the terror implicit in the revival meeting of this nature.)

76

(The Elders have come down to the front and put the dishpans on the table in front of the pulpit. Blitch raises his hand as soon as the Elders have returned to their seats, and, lifting his head, he closes his eyes tightly to pray. The choir hums in the background.)

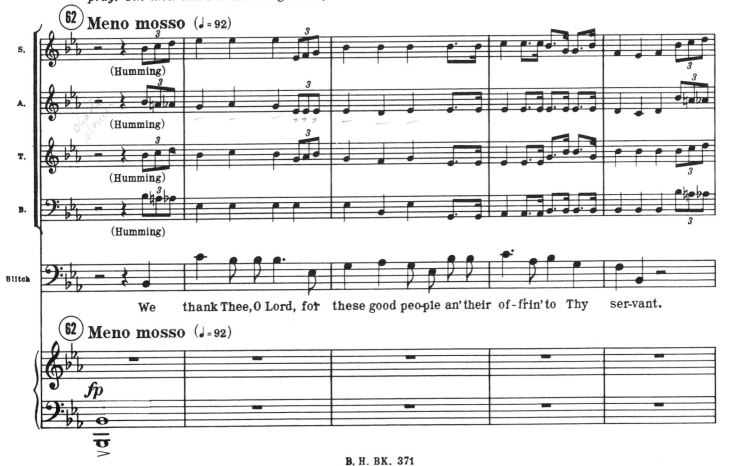

Bless them an' let this meet-in' to-night bring all the lost an' wand'rin home to the fold. Send

down the tongue of fire u-pon the heads of the damned 'til they won't find no peace 'cept in Thy cleans-in' blood.

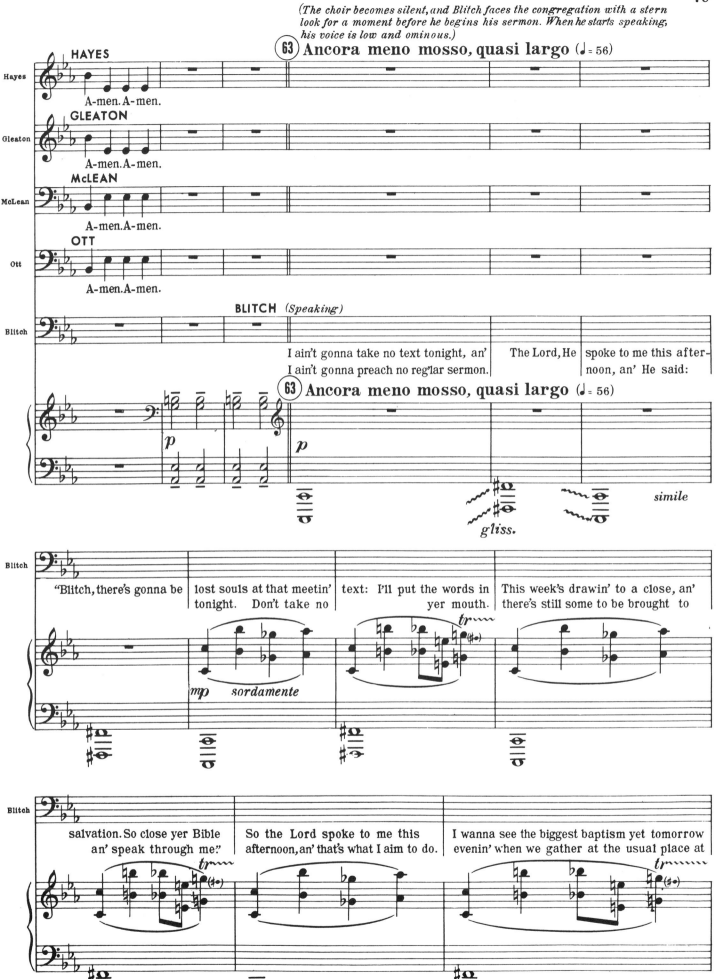

there he lay all sweat-in' with his eyes all star-in' with fright. He grabbed me by the hand and said: "They

tell me I'm a dy-in' man an' I might not git through the night. Seems like my

pore heart's done run down too soon an' I want-a make ev'-ry-thing right. I

ain't lived sich a bad life. I ain't drank, nor smoked, nor swore, but I'm

all a-feared o' dy-in'. I'm sure they's some-thin' more." Well, they

B. H. BK. 371

(Blitch nods to the choir, and they begin the hymn. Once again Blitch intermittently shouts over them. While before there was a strong element of the showman about him, now the showman has been tempered somewhat by an unexpected earnestness. Immediately after the "call", one or two boys and girls in their early teens shyly, with terrified eyes, leave their seats and trance-like walk down the aisle and kneel at the altar. Blitch lays his hands on their heads, throws his own back, and with closed eyes, speaks with the Almighty.)

(*The choir drones its plea again and again. The more intense their voices become, the more impassioned is the sound of Blitch's. Several more people come down to the altar with varying degrees of eagerness and hesitation. After a while the exodus to the altar ceases in spite of the continued protestations and urging of Blitch.*)

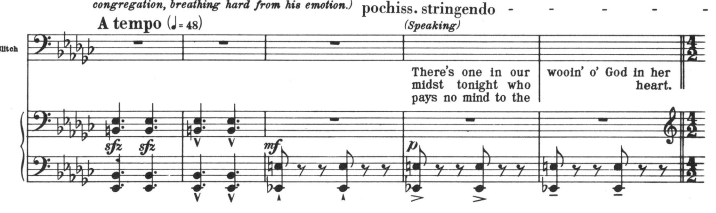

(Blitch suddenly turns to the choir and holding out his hand orders them to stop. He turns back around slowly to the congregation, breathing hard from his emotion.)

pochiss. stringendo - - - - -

A tempo (♩ = 48) *(Speaking)*

Blitch: There's one in our midst tonight who pays no mind to the wooin' o' God in her heart.

(The congregation, as a body, slowly turns around and stares at Susannah while Blitch continues to speak. There is no pity or concern in their looks; only the hard, cold stare of silent coercion. Susannah is immediately in great discomfort and looks straight ahead of her at the figure of Blitch.)

Andante moderato (♩=♩.) (♩ = 60)

Blitch: I've wrest-led with the dev-il fer her soul and prayed that she'd ac-cept the sav-in' grace o' the Lamb. An' put a-side her sin-ful an' shame-ful ways an' still she don't heed my plead-in'.

(Speaking)

Give over, sister, while the congregation sings one more verse. Publicly confess yer sins an' ask fergiveness o' the Lord an' these folks present tonight.

B. H. BK. 371

(The choir begins to sing its "invitation" hymn once again, and Blitch fixes his gaze upon Susannah. Slowly into his eyes and face comes an expression of intense desire bordering on lust. His voice also reflects what is happening inside him: instead of its heretofore peremptory and commanding quality, it now possesses a distinctly cajoling, almost caressing sound. Susannah watches him, transfixed.)

(Susannah moves slowly into the aisle and trance-like walks toward
Blitch, a confusion of fear, bewilderment and protest on her face. The

only sign of life about her is the periodic shaking of her head from side to side in weak dissent. The congregation is hushed and tense. A smile of triumph comes over Blitch's face as Susannah comes abreast of him and the change of expression in an instant shatters the spell for Susannah. She immediately comes to life and looks around her as if trapped. Suddenly she screams "no" and runs down the aisle and out into the night.)

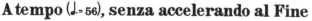

(Blitch's initial reaction is one of shock. He immediately regains control of himself, however, and the situation. Raising his hand and with a new note of anger, born of frustration, in his voice, he pronounces the benediction.)

A tempo (♩ = 56), senza accelerando al Fine

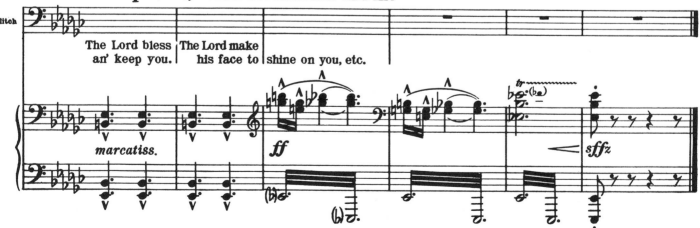

Scene: About an hour later. The scene is once more the front porch of the Polk house.
(Susannah is singing to herself as the curtain rises.)

*If desired, the first 2 or 4 bars of the accompaniment
may be played as an introduction and repeated as necessary.

pore bab - y fox lies all cold in his lair. His ma - ma jes' va - nished an'

left ____ him there, like a false-heart - ed lov - er, jes' like ___ my own, who

made me love him, then left ___ me a - lone. Come back, O sum - mer, come

back, blue flame! My heart wants warm-in', my bab - y a name. Come

back, O lov - er, if jes' fer a day. Turn bleak Dec - em - ber once more in - to ___ May. Come

(She breaks and sobs, fully released now for the first time, her face turned away from Blitch. He watches her and is momentarily defeated. Something akin to pity comes over his face, and when he speaks finally, his voice is heavy with weariness.)

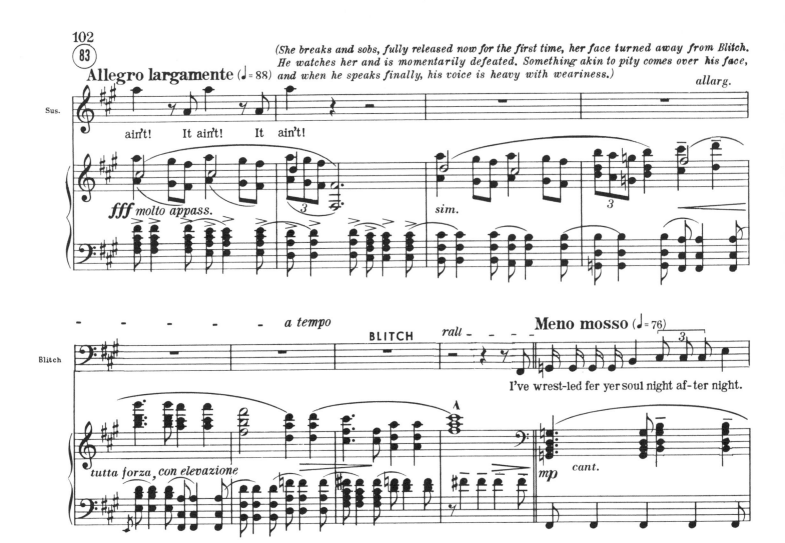

Allegro largamente (♩ = 88)

Sus.

ain't! It ain't! It ain't!

fff molto appass.

sim.

allarg.

a tempo

BLITCH *rall*

Meno mosso (♩ = 76)

Blitch

I've wrest-led fer yer soul night af-ter night.

tutta forza, con elevazione

mp cant.

(Susannah has covered her face with her hands, and although her body is still shaken with sobbing, she is quieter, a pathetic figure silhouetted against

molto rall. ─── **Largo** (♩=48)

Blitch

May-be to mor-row you'll come to the light.

p

pp ma marc.

the post, crumpled, helpless and alone. Blitch looks at her sadly a long time. Finally with weary hesitance and obviously fighting himself, he walks up the steps to her and puts his hands cautiously on her shoulders. Susannah stands inert and spent and in no way reacts to his closeness. The remainder of the scene should be weighted with exhaustion and defeat.)

p espr.

pp

need some-bo-dy I can love like oth-er folks 'cause it's a lone-some work I do.

(He brings her hand to rest on his shoulder and puts an arm around her. Susannah's arms hang slackly at her side. There is little sign of life about her, only the slow, weary shaking of her head while her eyes remain closed.)

85 **Più lento** (♩ = 48)

Will yer broth-er be home to night?

No. I'm so tired. I jes' cain't fight no more.

To herself

Almost a whisper

Let's go in-side.

(Blitch with his arm around her and her head on his shoulder moves her slowly to the door and into the shadows of the house.)

Scene Four

Scene: Saturday morning. It is once again the interior of New Hope church.
(As the curtain rises, Blitch is found kneeling. He is praying, and there is a terrible earnestness and anguish in the sound of his voice as well as an element of fear. His hands are clasped tightly together, and they from time to time emphasize his desperate sincerity. It should be immediately apparent that here is Blitch for the first time stripped of his bravado and evangelical trappings: a man terrified by his own image of a vengeful God.)

gone far a-way be-yond the sound of my cal-lin'. Re-turn and grant my tor-tured soul the balm of Thy for-give-ness.

fp e legato · *diminuendo* · *pp*

88 **Più mosso**

Blitch: **What shall I do if Thou de-sert me?** **Leave me not with this weight of sin op-**

f · *sempre cresc.*

allargando

Blitch: **pres-sin' me an' con-demn me not to the fires of hell. Re-turn, O Lord, I pray Thee, O re-**

cresc.

Molto deliberato

Blitch: **turn! And let this cup, if it be Thy will, pass from me.**

ffp · *mp*

(Blitch continues to kneel, his hands clasped, when the Elders and their wives come in the back door of the church, and watching Blitch, with a puzzled look, they slowly walk down the aisle. Susannah comes in quietly behind them, unobserved, seating herself as before on the back bench. She sits stiffly, her face expressionless, and there is nothing about her to suggest the youthfulness and

Tempo I (♩ = 72)   *rall.*

mp · *pp*

softness that has been apparent previously. As the Elders and their wives seat themselves, Blitch looks up, startled, and im-
mediately gets to his feet. He sees Susannah, and she returns his look evenly, without disdain or embarrassment. Blitch comes

around in front of the altar and stands in front of the group.) **BLITCH:**

Breth-ren an' sis-ter'n,   I asked you to come here this

morn-ing fer the pur-pose of right-in' a ter-rib-le wrong.   It's a bless-ed priv-i-lege___ fer the Lord to

let us make res-ti-tu-tion___ fer our er-rors while we are a-live.   An' we have all been in er-ror,

breth-ren an' sis-ter'n,   bad   er-ror.   The young wom-an what sits in the rear has been the

swear to you she's in - no - cent! She's   in - no - cent of the charg - es you've made.   Make

McLEAN *(Turning at the door)*

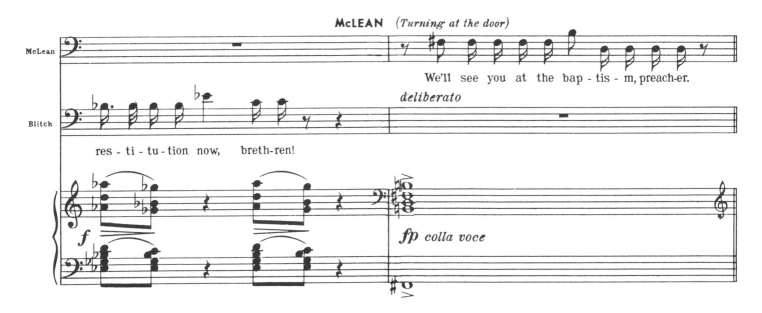

We'll see you at the bap - tis - m, preach - er.

deliberato

res - ti - tu - tion now,   breth - ren!

fp colla voce

(They leave haughtily ignoring Susannah who stares straight ahead. Blitch watches them go, his body taut and his face bewildered, unable to believe that he has failed to convince them. After a moment, Susannah begins laughing to herself, short

Più mosso (♩ = 112)

㉑

laughs that hardly rise out of her throat and do nothing to alter the immobility of her face. Blitch, hearing the strange laughter, looks at her and brokenly walks down the aisle, gesturing helplessly. Susannah looks straight ahead.)

rall.   **Adagio molto sostenuto** (♩ = 52)

p elegiaco

SUSANNAH (*Flatly, without looking at him*)

Yeah. I heard y'.

Sus.

Blitch
I tried, Su-san-nah; y'heard me.
I'll

mp < *mf* > *p*

(*Blitch starts to answer, then realizes that
there is nothing to say. Susannah stands up
and moves into the aisle. Blitch puts his
hand on her shoulder, as if to detain her, and
she jerks away from him with a shudder.*)

(*Speaking*) (*Venomously*)

How? Don't tech me.

make it up to y'. I swear I will.
Fer-

cresc. *f* *p* *pp* *mf* > *pp*

(*Susannah exits, and Blitch watches her go. Falling on his knees, sobbing, he grasps the arm of
the pew for support and cries out in an anguished voice*)

(*She starts out, and Blitch calls after her in a
broken voice*)

(*Turning to Blitch,
speaking*)

poco più mosso

Fergive? I've forgot
what that word means.

give me, Su-san-nah. Please try an' fer-give me.

poco più mosso

dim. *sfz* *p* *mf* *f*

92 **Largamente** (♩ = 60)

Blitch
O Lord, if it be Thy will, let this cup pass from me.

fp *fp* *p* < *ff* *fz* *fz*

8va below

Scene Five

Scene: The front porch of the Polk house. It is sundown of the same day.
(Susannah is discovered standing stiffly against one of the porch posts, staring vacantly ahead of her. There is a time of silence in contrast to her singing in Scene Three and this, coupled with the rather rigid, in-grown stance, suggests something of the change which has taken place in her since the previous scene.
After a moment, Sam comes on-stage with a bulging crocus-sack slung over one shoulder and a shotgun carried under the other arm. He is slightly drunk, and his spirits are high.)

(Tentatively, as if not expecting to be answered)

(Susannah walks slowly onto the porch, trance-like, her whole attitude

sempre accelerando

Sus. Sam... Sam...

(Her body stiffens, and her face becomes

99 Allegro deciso (♩. = 92)

revealing growing terror. She pauses at the steps and screams.)

Sam!

Sus.

sempre f

mask-like. She stands immobilized and rooted, awaiting with a terrible certainty, the inevitable.)

(A shot blasts the night air in the distance and Susannah stands transfixed for a moment. Then slowly, moving only her head, she turns toward the rack where the gun had lain. Seeing it gone, she arrests her motion and once again stands rigid. Slowly her hands rise and cover her face. Suddenly, she breaks, falling to her knees and crying out.)

Meno mosso (♩. = 56)

SUSANNAH

Sus.

(SHOT)

sffz *sffz* *ppp* *molto crescendo*

(The sound of voices is heard in the distance. Susannah stands rigidly against the porch post, her face becoming stern and set.)

B. H. BK. 371

(The mob led by the Elders comes on stage and by this time their voices are deafening. The voices soften as the Elders speak but the chanting continues steadily and ominously in the background.)

this was the worst of all to be-hold.

OTT

The preach-er was yer friend he was, for true. Yer

(Susannah begins to laugh mockingly, and the laughter con-tinues through the succeeding lines.)

HAYES

Y'd might as well o' killed him yer-self as had him killed.

name he called with the last breath he drew.

(The mob begins to move toward Susannah who is shrieking with laughter. Their mood becomes angrier.)

(As they close in on her, she abruptly stops laughing and shouts.)

105 Poco meno mosso, molto marcato

out! Git out! You cain't run me off my place till I'm read-y to leave, an' that'll be some time to come. So git

(The mob stops suddenly, surprised at her vehemence, and then begins coming towards her again. She whirls, runs into the house and is immediately out again with the gun Sam left her. She points it menacingly at the mob.)

più largamente   **Come sopra**

out! Git out!   Git a-way from here   a-fore I

(As the crowd disappears, Susannah walks over and puts the gun on the rack. As she does so, she notices Little Bat who has sneaked upstage, and her laughing stops. Little Bat looks at her wide-eyed and frightened. Slowly Susannah walks to the post and leans against it, seductively. Her tone of voice now completely changes, and her manner is spuriously soft and helpless, obscuring only for Little Bat her fierce contempt for him.)

quasi parlando

(He comes over to her tentatively.)

SUSANNAH

Come on o-ver, Lit-tle Bat. Don't be scared. I won't hurt y'. I'm lone-some. Come an' love me up some.

p e sordo

pp

(Little Bat walks hesitantly up the steps and stops momentarily. As he comes nearer to her,

Come on. Don't be a-fraid. I'm all by my-self now an' y' know I was al-lers good to y'. Y'

(Susannah fights a loathing and revulsion to his closeness.)

(He goes to her and puts his arms around her, and as he does so, Susannah slaps him viciously across the face.

said so yer-self. So come on. Come on.

mp molto crescendo

Little Bat, holding his cheek, runs yelping down the steps and across the yard. Susannah once again reels with laughter and holding her sides moves to the door, watching Little Bat as she does so. When he is gone, her strident laughter vanishes as quickly as it began. She turns around, straightens her body in the doorway and remains standing there, an inviolably strong and inexorably lonely prisoner of a self-imposed exile. The curtain falls.)

108 Molto largamente (♩ = 60)

sfz fp ff fff ffz ffz fz sffz

sfz fp ff fff

fp